S. Pe

Co

N

··· 9DU

019**02** 558600

Ransom Neutron Stars
The Giant Jigsaw
by Cath Jones
Illustrated by Graham Robson

Published by Ransom Publishing Ltd.
Unit 7, Brocklands Farm, West Meon, Hampshire GU32 1JN, UK
www.ransom.co.uk

ISBN   978 178591 446 1
First published in 2017

The Giant Jigsaw

Cath Jones

Illustrated by Graham Robson

Ben punched the air.

"Hooray!" he said. "I've nearly finished another giant jigsaw puzzle!"

The jigsaw puzzle filled the table.

"Jigsaw puzzles are a waste of time,"
his wife said. "Look at the time. You
need to go to work!"

Ben looked at the clock.

"Oh dear!" he said. "I'm late!"

He ran out of the house.

"Come back," said his wife. "You need your broom!"

Ben laughed and came back.

Ben swept up the leaves in the street.

He put them into a big bag.

He swept up bottles and cans
and put them into a bigger bag.

He swept up all the litter in the street.

"Good morning Ben!" said the baker.

"Thank you for sweeping up our street."

"That's okay," Ben said with a smile.

"Good morning Ben!" said the lollipop lady. "Please will you look in that dustbin? It's full to the brim!"

"I'll do it now," Ben said with a smile.

A big bag filled the dustbin.

"This is very odd," Ben said. "I wonder what's in the bag."

He lifted out the bag and put it in his cart.

"It's time for lunch," Ben said. "I'm going home. Goodbye!"

He took the cart and the big bag home.

"Hello!" said his wife. "What's in that big bag?"

Ben tipped up the bag.

Lots of little bits of paper fell out onto the table.

"It's rubbish!" his wife said.

"No," said Ben. "It's money."

"But the money is all cut up!" his wife said. "So it's rubbish."

Ben sat at the table.

"This money is like a giant jigsaw puzzle!" he said with a smile.

"Rubbish!" said his wife.

But Ben stuck together all the bits of paper.

He punched the air.

"Hooray!" he said. "I've finished this giant jigsaw puzzle!"

The money filled the table!

"Wow!" said his wife. "Maybe Jigsaw puzzles aren't a waste of time."

Two weeks later ...

THE END

Have you read?

Awesome ATAs

by Kathryn White

Wolves

by Jill Atkins

Have you read?

Fit for Love

by Elizabeth Dale

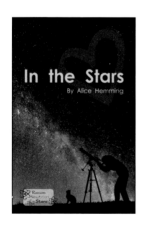

In the Stars

by Alice Hemming

Ransom Neutron Stars

The Giant Jigsaw
Word count **319**

Blue Book Band

<table>
<tr><td colspan="4">**Phonics**</td></tr>
<tr>
<td>*Phonics 1*</td>
<td>Not Pop, Not Rock
Go to the Laptop Man
Gus and the Tin of Ham</td>
<td>*Phonics 2*</td>
<td>Deep in the Dark Woods
Night Combat
Ben's Jerk Chicken Van</td>
</tr>
<tr>
<td>*Phonics 3*</td>
<td>GBH
Steel Pan Traffic Jam
Platform 7</td>
<td>*Phonics 4*</td>
<td>The Rock Show
Gaps in the Brain
New Kinds of Energy</td>
</tr>
</table>

<table>
<tr><td colspan="4">**Book bands**</td></tr>
<tr>
<td>*Pink*</td>
<td>Curry!
Free Runners
My Toys</td>
<td>*Red*</td>
<td>Shopping with Zombies
Into the Scanner
Planting My Garden</td>
</tr>
<tr>
<td>*Yellow*</td>
<td>Fit for Love
The Lottery Ticket
In the Stars</td>
<td>*Blue*</td>
<td>Awesome ATAs
Wolves
The Giant Jigsaw</td>
</tr>
<tr>
<td>*Green*</td>
<td>Fly, May FLY!
How to Start Your Own
Crazy Cult
The Care Home</td>
<td>*Orange*</td>
<td>Text Me
The Last Soldier
Best Friends</td>
</tr>
</table>